TH
MYSTERY
OF
ERNIE TAYLOR'S
ABDOMEN
AND OTHER
STORIES

Jonathan Evans

The Mystery of Ernie Taylor's Abdomen and Other Stories
First published 2020 by Tangent Books

Tangent Books
Unit 5.16 Paintworks, Bristol BS4 3EH
0117 972 0645
www.tangentbooks.co.uk
richard@tangentbooks.co.uk

ISBN 978-1-910089-98-9

Author: Jonathan Evans
Typesetting and cover design: Eva Mason
Production: Nicky Coates

A CIP record of this book is available at the British Library.

contents

For
Madge and Harry

Chapter 1: Beginnings

I was born in the winter of 1949 in the small mining town of Kirkby in Ashfield in north Nottinghamshire. The town was dominated by the Summit Colliery whose enormous black pit tip glowered over everything. This is the setting for these tales.

From what I recall of those very early days, my life was full of wonder. My grandfather, Judd, was an ex-miner who prided himself on his learning. I remember him constantly telling me that I would grow up to be a scholar – I had no idea then what a scholar was, but I assumed it had something to do with the sailing picture he had on the wall of the living room, and I would stare at this as I sat on his knee and chatted with him.

My grandmother, Ada, was as wrinkled as a month-old lettuce and had a wicked way with stories. The favourite ones were about a character called Brer Rabbit. In her version of events, Brer Rabbit's nemesis, Brer Fox, always ended up with 'a pitchfork up his backside' or with 'his arse on fire'. This amused me greatly, but upset my mother who like to think of herself and the family as middle class and frowned on any sort of bad language.

At the back of the house were about three acres of land. This was full of orchards, allotments, greenhouses and chicken runs, and was paradise for young children. I remember hearing stories about the Garden of Eden, and was sure that this was it. In summer, with my sister Sue and my brother Richard, we would stage pitched battles with soft fruit, and launch apples and pears at each other from homemade catapults. My younger brothers, Nick, Simon and Adam, were born after we moved from that house and so missed out on all this innocent fun.

My dad worked as an osteopath and naturopath, and this brought stream of visitors which encouraged my interest in people and the stories they told. My mum was constantly on the go cooking, washing and ironing and generally keeping us all afloat.

My memories go right back, further than most people believe possible. I remember, for example, lying in bed between my parents in the house where I was born. The sun was streaming in through the window and I felt warm, loved and comfortable.

Now folks will tell you that this is a false memory, but a few years ago the house went up for sale and, when I went for a look around, the room was still pretty much as I remember it.

Another early memory has me riding in my pram. It was

hot and my grandfather was pushing me. We stopped. He put something in my mouth which tasted wonderful. I remember that I was dressed all in white and I guess it must have been a knitted suit that was probably my mother's pride and joy. My mouth became sticky and my fingers were in the stickiness and the taste was joy beyond joy. Then the stickiness and the pleasure were everywhere. This thing, this taste, was wonderful. The pram bounced along, and I was in taste heaven. I didn't know it then, but this must have been my first encounter with chocolate.

I also remember the stage in my early childhood when I thought adults were a totally different kind of creature to me. I recall looking up at them and seeing their heads wave around in the air like flowers in the breeze. I guess this must have been because I was so unsteady on my feet, and it was actually me who was wobbling around. I also remember two other very magical experiences: the first, when I was about two years old, looking at my brother and sister and then at the adults and gradually realising that one day I would turn into one of these wonderful, big creatures; and the second, when I was about four and my older brother taught me to read one morning with my copy of a children's comic.

Anyway, that's enough background. I hope you enjoy the stories of my misadventures as much as I did the first time around.

Chapter 2:
Love Hearts

I remember hiding in the dank, smelly toilet cubicle, waiting for them to come and get me. I was eight years old and absolutely terrified.

How had things come to this? Well, a couple of days earlier, I had flattened Ralph Vardy after he had picked on me on my way home. Unwisely, this led me to announce that I was the best fighter in the school. Nobody seemed to take much notice of this claim apart from Mary O'Brien who sat opposite me in class, and who was remarkable for her flame-red hair and her neverending supply of sweets.

Mary seemed to take a shine to me after the Ralph Vardy incident, and she spread the word of my fighting prowess as rapidly as possible in between giving me sidelong glances and embarrassed smiles. I remember once finding a packet of Refreshers on my desk and looking at Mary, but she turned away, crimson from head to foot.

At playtime the next afternoon, things took a turn for the worse when John Rabbit came running up to me told me that Barry Gascoigne, who really was the best fighter in the school, was looking for me. Barry was two years older, and I'm sure he was a cross between a Neanderthal and a gorilla.

My insides churned, and I decided to lie low until the bell rang. My best option, it seemed, was to hide in the boys' toilets. I ran in and found an empty stall and locked the door behind me. I waited in the dark, my knees knocking. From my bolthole I could hear the screams, whoops and laughs and cries of the other kids in the playground and, for a few moments, although desperately alone, I felt safe.

It is amazing when you're scared just how vivid sounds can be. I could hear and recognise individual voices – the girls playing their skipping games, the boys machine-gunning German soldiers and then, clearly but a long way away, Barry Gasgcoine asking again and again, "Where is he?" Nobody seemed to know and I thought I just might escape. Then I heard the reedy voice of Mary O'Brien.

"He's in the toilet," she squeaked and my stomach clenched and almost turned itself inside out.

Into the toilet they marched. "We know you're in there, open up."

I kept quiet, hoping they wouldn't find me and would go away,but they didn't. I heard the doors being kicked open, one by one. They arrived at mine. My heart sank. A pause, then they started banging and kicking the door and, for some reason panic, maybe, I opened up and they dragged me out.

Barry marched me with his hands on the scruff of my neck. My mind was in a whirl and I was terrified. I knew that what was going to happen next was going to be dreadfully painful.

He stood me up against a brick wall.

My every sense was on high alert. I noticed details in the brickwork, the drainpipe that I'd never noticed before. I looked at the sky. It was blue, with fluffy clouds rolling across it. How could that be? I thought to myself, doesn't God know what is going on? Isn't he going to rescue me? Out of the corner of my eye I could see Mary O'Brien looking on with interest.

"Did you say you were the best fighter in the school?" Barry demanded. Mary listened expectantly.
I looked at the ground, then, in a very quiet voice answered
"Yes."
"Are you?" he asked.
"Yes," I said weakly. I'm not sure why I said this. Perhaps it was pride. Whatever the reason, Barry did not appreciate it.

With one hand he grabbed me around the throat and pushed me hard against the wall, then he pulled his right fist back. This was going to hurt. As his fist sped towards me, time stood still. I then suddenly remembered my brother Richard once telling me "If anybody hits you, just duck."
'Duck'? What did he mean? How could a duck help me?

I shut my eyes and waited for the punch to arrive. But before it did, something else struck me. I suddenly understood what to duck meant and, at the last micro-second, with my eyes still tightly closed, I moved my head out of the way.

The next thing that happened was that I heard a scream of pain. I thought it was me at first but, when I opened my eyes, I could see Barry Gasgoine holding a bloody fist and leaping about in agony. I seized my chance and thumped him with all my might. His nose exploded in a fountain of blood and he ran. I chased him all the way back to the school building where he sought sanctuary.

I was elated. John Rabbit and Clive Kirk were patting me on the back when Mary O'Brien came up and said "I always knew you would beat him."

She smiled at me and slipped something into my hand. It was a sweet, a love heart. I looked down and read the inscription. 'Love Hurts'. I put it in my mouth and ran off to play football with my mates.

Chapter 3:
The Mystery of Ernie Taylor's Abdomen

Like most young kids, I used to love looking through the dictionary for dirty words. Quite often, however, it seemed to act as a moral policeman and gave definitions that were plainly false. I remember once, for example, looking up 'masturbation', a word I'd heard in the playground, and expecting to find up a description of some exciting activity.

What I found, however, was a puzzling statement about something called 'bodily self-pollution' or 'onanism'. When I looked up onanism it sent me back in a circle to 'masturbation'. I was greatly disappointed and was convinced that the authors could learn an awful lot from my mate John Rabbit who seemed to be the world's leading authority on the topic, at least amongst eight year olds.

During my pioneering dictionary studies I was in year two of my primary school. Our teacher was an old lady called Miss Pike. I knew she was ancient because she had taught my mum some forty years earlier and, as my mum said, she was no spring chicken, even in those days.

Miss Pike had clearly enjoyed better health, and spent most of the time talking to herself and arching her eyebrows towards an invisible presence.

The highlight of our week was the Tuesday morning nature programme broadcast by the BBC. In preparation for this, Miss Pike would go to a big cupboard and pull out an enormous rectangular radio. Made of wood, it housed a large circular speaker and a single on-off switch, this also doubled as the volume control.

Two minutes before the scheduled start, Miss Pike would switch it on. It hummed for about half a minute while it was warming up – this was what all radios did in those days. Eventually music would emerge while we waited expectantly.

"Good morning children, this is a BBC Home Service Schools broadcast. Nature Study, 'the Vole', presented by Arthur Garlick."

Every week was a different topic. One day we had a programme entitled 'Tits' by Christine Dudley which was disappointing. We learnt about thrushes, earthworms, lions and elephants and afterwards we had to do a colour drawing in our exercise books and write a page on the subject. I still have a copy of an extra-terrestrial creature which I have labelled the Mistlethrush. In its beak it is carrying an object which looks a bit like a hand grenade but which is supposed to be a snail and, underneath the drawing in spidery red letters, is a comment, 'excellent' and a red star.

John Rabbit, quite appropriately, was the resident class expert on wildlife. He would bring in slow worms, birds' eggs and the skeletal remains of various mammals – all of which he could identify. He was also a skilled illustrator, and I was envious of both his knowledge and his artistry. He loved the outdoors and could talk at length about how to preserve birds' eggs and different ways of poaching game. John also shared my passion for football, and he and I regularly swapped Chix bubble gum cards of famous players.

One particular nature programme sticks in my mind. It was entitled 'The Fly'. I must admit I was rather hoping for 'The Man-Eating Tiger' or 'The Killer Shark' and, partly because of my lack of interest, the stuffiness of the room or the buzzing sounds that came from the radio, I began to drift off.

It was then that I heard it. "The male fly mounts the female and transfers sperm from his abdomen…"

SPERM? I sat bolt upright, was I imagining things? I looked at John Rabbit, he was drawing on his desk; he obviously hadn't heard.

I nudged John. "These flies are 'doing it'" I whispered.
He gave me a strange look.

"Listen."

But that was it – the next bit was about eggs, and then maggots, and eventually something more about flies.

After the lesson was over I explained to John what the programme was all about, but he seemed more interested in the possible uses of maggots to catch fish.

Convinced I was on the right track, I sought out my dictionary as soon as I could. I furtively searched for my new word of the week, 'abdomen' and, sure enough, it was there, 'The part of the body containing the digestive and reproductive organs'.

Just below this entry there was also reference to something called the 'abdominal thrust'. These two bits of information convinced me. Although the adults writing the dictionary were obviously trying to confuse me, reference to reproduction was a dead giveaway. The abdomen was clearly a posh name for a man's willy, and this was confirmed by the fact that it was used in something called an abdominal thrust – which even an idiot could work out was a scientific term for shagging.

Over the next few weeks the word 'abdomen' cropped up in the news from time to time. I almost choked on my breakfast one morning hearing that a British soldier in Cyprus had been 'shot in the abdomen'.

The reporter elaborated, "Corporal Smith was hit in the abdomen by three bullets, he is said to be in a comfortable condition".

Jesus Christ! Three bullets in the todger. How unlucky is that? It's a wonder it wasn't shot off entirely. How the hell could he be 'comfortable'? Oh, and another thing, how big must his abdomen have been to cop not one, but three bullets? I was both intrigued and impressed.

Then we come to Ernie Taylor. Some weeks before, I had obtained his Chix footballer card as a swap from John Rabbit.

According to the information on the back, Ernie was not only a 'former submariner' who fought in the Second World War, but an 'industrious and creative inside forward', who at the time the cards were printed played for Blackpool. He had not only served his country with distinction, but had also won a couple of FA Cup winner's medals.

After the Munich air crash of 1958 he had, however, joined Manchester United whom my team, Nottingham Forest, were due to play that weekend. I had taken a shine to him and was looking forward to seeing him in the flesh.

On the Saturday, as I was about to leave for the game, I heard an almost unbelievable item on the sports news.

"Manchester United's Ernie Taylor has had to pull out of today's game because he has torn an abdominal muscle."

Christ almighty, how did he do that? I thought. My mind boggled. It must have undergone an enormous strain to TEAR it. What on earth was he doing with it?

This thought was immediately followed by another. Was he by himself when it got damaged, or was there anybody else involved?

In either case it was highly embarrassing. What did his family and friends think? If it was me and I had damaged my nether regions, I certainly wouldn't want the world and its mother to know.

On match days I caught the supporters' bus from the bottom of Mutton Hill. As I boarded it that day I was greeted by Gwen, a lovely woman aged about thirty-five who collected the bus fares and the club subs. Because I was so young, Gwen used to keep a special eye out for me and make sure I got to and from the ground safely. She would also talk to me about the latest football news. To my great embarrassment, on that particular day she homed right in.

" Ernie Taylor is out then"
"Yes"
"Tore a muscle didn't he?"
"Yes"
"Where was it?"
"In his abdomen," I blurted out.

I sensed that everybody on the bus was listening and I turned a dark shade of crimson. It was as though I'd mentioned the word 'gynaecologist', which John Rabbit had introduced to the class to a couple of weeks earlier. That was the day that John told us that when he left school he no longer work wanted to work down the pit like his dad, but was hoping to become some sort of doctor.

"Mm," someone behind me muttered. "After Billy Gray did that he was never the same man again."

What? My hero Billy had also injured his todger? There was no mention of that in his 'Chix famous footballer' entry, nor in the article I had read about him in last year's edition of the Charles Buchan Soccer Annual. I spent the rest of the journey wondering what other secrets adults were keeping from me.

When we got to the ground I made my way straight to the main entrance, where I would regularly try and spot players arriving for the game. I timed it just as the United coach rolled in.

Lots of supporters raced towards the players, autograph books in hand, trying to obtain the signatures of their favourites.

I was only looking for one man, Ernie Taylor. I knew from my card collection that he sported a brylcreemed quiff and was quite short, only five feet four inches tall. Pretty useful if you were working in a submarine, but otherwise a bit of a social disadvantage. He was the last person off the coach and I recognized him immediately. I looked carefully to see if I could see any evidence of his injury. He walked rather stiffly and I was visually scanning his trousers when he saw me looking at him. He winced as he walked over.

"Keep your pecker up, Ernie," someone shouted. Ernie smiled wanly. I suddenly felt very sorry for this man who was bearing his cross so bravely.

He took my autograph book and scribbled in it.

"Sorry you're not playing," I said, hoping to cheer him up.

"Never mind, worse things happen at sea," he replied and sauntered into the dressing rooms.

Yes, worse things did happen at sea – Ernie would know that after his time in the war. Worse things also happened on land as Corporal Smith would no doubt testify.

Maybe the adults who were keen to ignore Ernie's embarrassing injury were right to do so, after all, there were many more important things going in the world weren't there?

Chapter 4:
I Had a Dream

We were walking along Balfour Street when my brother Richard began telling me a strange tale which both scared and intrigued me.

"Last night, I had a really odd dream. We were walking along, just around here and," he paused for a moment and looked around "see that drainpipe up ahead?"

I nodded

"Well, in my dream there was a pound note wedged behind it; it seemed so real. I could feel the breeze, it was even spitting with rain."

As he said this I noticed, for the first time, a few drops pattering on the ground.

"And you were here with me, just like you are now" he said.

That was some dream. A bit like the dreams those folks in the Bible used to have, I thought. You know the sort of thing, plagues of locusts, seven fat years and seven lean years, plagues of flies, frogs and who knows what. Dreams certainly were mysterious and occasionally, maybe, just sometimes, they might come true.

Richard had a far-away look in his eye. He was obviously

thinking about the pound note. "Just imagine if there was one there."

"Yes, we could buy the chemistry set." This thought came to me as if by magic.

Richard had had his heart set on a magnificent chemistry set which was on sale at Bray's, the only toy shop in Kirkby. For the last week or so, ever since he had seen it, it had been his obsession. He had even taken me to the shop twice to look at it. Unfortunately though, at seventeen shillings and sixpence, it was way out of our price bracket, and my mum had made it quite clear that it was beyond her price bracket as well.

"It would have been nice, wouldn't it?" Richard went on. "Did you see what it had? Sulphur, charcoal, saltpetre – lots of stuff. We could have blown things up, made stink bombs. It would have been great."

"Come on, let's go home," he said sadly and turned away to walk down Forest Street.

A thought struck me. What if the dream were true?

"Why don't we look?"

Richard wasn't interested. He seemed about to cry.

"It was only a dream. there'll be nothing there. Come on, let's go."

I felt sorry for my big brother and tried to cheer him up. "Come on," I said, "it's only a bit further, we might as well check."

Richard shrugged his shoulders and followed as I ran to the drainpipe.

The pipe was old, but had recently been repainted with black enamel. I looked carefully and felt around the back and I remember the roughness where rust was bubbling to the surface. Almost immediately I saw something. At the base, wedged against the wall, was some scrunched paper. My heart skipped, but as I pulled it out, I realised that it was just an old sweet bag. I felt a wave of disappointment but didn't give up. I continued to look high and low. There were a few cobwebs, some old twigs but, alas, no sign of the fabled pound note.

Richard looked at me consolingly. "Never mind," he said. "At least we tried." We turned and walked away in silence.

Richard spoke first. "What would dad say?"

I shrugged, not sure how to answer.

He smiled, "If at first you don't succeed, try, try and try again. I'm going back just to check that you didn't miss anything."

We retraced our steps. Already Richard seemed more positive. He looked up and down and then, just as I had earlier, felt round the back of the pipe.

"No, ...nothing there," and then, a pause...

"Hold on a minute."

He pulled his hand from behind the pipe and there, between his fingers, was a crumpled piece of paper, a pound note.

I couldn't believe my eyes. How had I missed it? Its lucky my brother had the good sense to do a double check.

"That's incredible. I can't wait to tell mum."

Richard's expression changed. He was suddenly serious.

"You can't tell anyone, especially not mum and dad."

"Why not?" I protested.

"They'll never believe you. They will think that you pinched it or something. Telling them will just get you into trouble."

"No, we must tell them, it's incredible."

Richard looked at me again.

"No, adults just don't like to believe that that things like this really happen."

Even if they do believe you, they will make us take the money down to the police station. The police will ask you lots of questions and, even if you don't get into trouble with them, we'll never see the money again. It would be safest if we just kept quiet about it."

This, I had to admit, seemed to have a certain logic; after all, the last thing that I wanted was to get tangled up with the police. Maybe this pound note wasn't such a wonderful find after all.

Richard was on the same wavelength.

"Maybe we should just throw it away."

This seemed a bit drastic, and I said as much.

"Well, if they find the pound note in your pocket they will want to know where you got it from."

"So, what can we do?" I asked.

Richard thought. "Well, we could spend it."

I suddenly had a brain wave – of course, why not buy the chemistry set?

It took us quite a while to get to Bray's. It was about three-quarters of a mile, all the way down Diamond Avenue, past the Regent Cinema, along Station Street, over the level crossing and just down the hill from the police station.

Bray's was, by some distance, the biggest shop in town. Strangely though, it never seemed to have any customers. The ground floor was given over almost entirely to furniture and pram sales ,while the toyshop was on the first floor.

Once upstairs, we homed in on the chemistry set. I remember that for a second or two we considered buying a cheaper version at fourteen and six, but quickly agreed that we wanted the best. A shop assistant, a woman, smart and quite severe looking wearing black-framed spectacles, came over.

We told her what we wanted and she looked concerned.
"Do your parents know that you're buying this?"
Richard, who was an adept liar, replied, "Yes, its my birthday. My grandmother gave me a pound note and told me to get whatever I wanted."
The assistant seemed to be weighing this up. Then she smiled and said, "Well that's all right then. Just be careful with it."
She wrapped our prize carefully in brown paper, took us to the till and gave us our change, half a crown.

I thought that we would go straight back to my grandad's shed and begin blowing things up, but Richard was already thinking ahead.

"We have to get rid of the evidence."

Now, 'evidence' was a word I'd come across quite a bit. Every week on TV, Fabian of the Yard could be seen in his black Humber Hawk squealing at high speed round the streets of London looking for 'evidence' which usually ended up sending folks to the gallows or, almost as bad, to Dartmoor.

So, when Richard mentioned 'evidence' I understandably felt a bit uncomfortable.

He expanded on his concerns. "We've got to get rid of that half a crown. It's evidence."

I was confused, after all we had the world's biggest chemistry set – wasn't that 'evidence' as well?

Richard could see I was uncomfortable and was struggling to understand. I was also aware that the police station was rather close and I began to feel that I was getting out of my depth with all this.

"Look, it's simple," he said. "We'll go to Purdey's, get some matches, we need them for our experiments, and we'll spend the rest on sweets."

Purdey's was a newsagents on Kingsway, not really on our route, but it was well known for its laissez-faire attitude to selling stuff like matches and lighter fuel to young kids.

When we got there Richard started mooching around near the magazine section. He picked one up 'Health and Efficiency' – the world's leading naturist magazine." On the cover was a photograph of a naked young woman playing beachball with a balding bespectacled man who had forgotten to put on any clothes. Luckily, his lower half was obscured by the strategic placement of a lawnmower. Inside was an article entitled 'Hiking in the Pennines'.

The main character must have been made of stern stuff, because all she was wearing was a pair of hiking boots and a chiffon scarf. Her companion, a portly middle-aged man, was wearing white plimsoles and a curious expression and, presumably in case of inclement weather, was carrying around a rather large thermos flask which he held just below his stomach.

Having had a quick look, I must admit I was more interested in the latest edition of Charlie Buchan's 'Football Monthly' but Richard was insistent.

He gave me the money and pushed the magazine into my hand. "Get this and ten Park Drive. Don't forget the matches."

As I walked up to the counter, Mrs Purdey greeted me with a smile. She knew me well, and I saw her quite often because she was a patient of my dad.

"What is it today?" she asked smiling, "the Beezer or the Dandy?"

I reddened and pushed my purchases towards her, feeling mightily embarrassed.

"I can't sell you this," she said looking distastefully at the beachball frolics. "It's for grownups."

I thought for a moment.

"It's not for me, it's for my dad"

Mrs Purdey looked rather shocked. Quickly I realised I needed a bit more detail.

"It's his birthday."

This sort of popped into my mind and was out before I could stop it.

Amazingly it did the trick. Mrs Purdey put my purchases in a paper bag. We left and headed back to blow things up.

Back in my grandad's shed things were getting rather toxic. The air was thick with the fumes of burning sulphur and the stench of rotten eggs. Added to this was the acrid smell of Park Drive cigarettes. We were just lighting another when the call came for us to return to the house for dinner.

We trooped into the kitchen to eat, and could hear my mum in the hallway talking to one of my dad's patients on the phone. Apparently, the caller was cancelling an appointment, something that happened only very occasionally.

Sitting round the dining table I quickly became aware that something was wrong. If the atmosphere in the shed had been toxic, here it was lethal. My grandmother was in a foul mood. Something about the milkman.

She kept asking, "Did you see it?"

See what? I had no idea what she was talking about. Whatever it was that I hadn't seen was making her really angry.

"I put it out with the milk bottles this morning and it's gone; someone's taken it." She glared at everyone.

Just then my mum came in. "Mrs Purdey's had to cancel her appointment. If it's not one bloody thing it's another."

"Bloody" – did I hear correctly? – my mum swearing? What on earth was going on?

We ate in silence. Something was really wrong. Then it came out.

Grandma spoke in an odd way. It was as if she was talking to herself, but her anger was clear from the tone of her voice. "I put a pound note under the milk bottles this morning and it's gone."

For a second I thought I could hear the siren on Inspector Fabian's squad car and looked over at Richard.

His face was a picture of serenity, and then I caught a sort of look from him, subtle but very precise, 'whatever happens, don't say anything'.

He finished his food in record time and asked to leave the table.

As he got down he grabbed me by the arm.

"Let's go and play," he said.

What he really meant was, 'let's go and lie low.', I knew that that was what all great criminals did. We left quickly and prayed that things would die down.

Chapter 5:
DH Lawrence, the Lion Tamer and the Doctor's Wife

It was the summer of 1961, the last year of primary school. I didn't know it then, but it was the last summer that I'd spend with my mates, John Rabbit, Clive Kirk and Michael Atherton. After our eleven-plus exams we were all heading to different schools, and our paths were destined never to cross again.

It seems strange in a small place like Kirkby that you could go for years without bumping into people, but in those days that was how it was.

That summer 'Ox' Smith had somehow managed to get hold of a rather dog-eared copy of 'Lady Chatterley's Lover' by DH Lawrence, a book which had been the subject, a year earlier, of a famous pornography trial at the Old Bailey. It told a story as old as time about a working-class bloke having a forbidden love affair with an aristocratic woman.

We spent lots of that summer in the shed at the top of the Acre, just next to the football pitch playing kickabout and smoking Park Drive cigarettes. We were a motley crew. I was among the youngest, but others like Ox, Ray Hayes and Stuart Boam were a couple of years older. Ray, in particular, seemed older than the rest. He had no dad, had only one lung, and had had to grow up smart and fast. In our football games he was always Nat Lofthouse, the 'Lion of Vienna'. We liked Ray.

It was in the shed that Ox would read selected extracts from the book. The juicy bits were easy to find, you just opened it at random and it would fall open at the most visited pages.

The erotic charge of the novel was, however, somewhat dissipated by Ox's unique narrative style. I recall him describing the scene in which Mellors, the gamekeeper, seemed to have a problem with a 'flame in his lions'.

We were all puzzled. In an earlier passage there had been some boring stuff about chickens, but no mention of lions.

Ray grabbed the book. "It says loins," he said, "not lions."

Ox went on unabashed, "He had a flame in his loins but it leapt and leapt downwards, circling his knees."

"Jesus," I thought, "it's circling his knees," and I felt rather inadequate.

As Ox continued, something odd seemed to happen to Mellors. Just as he was about to get down to business with Lady Chatterley, "Compassion flamed in his bowels for her," according to Ox.

"That's not very polite, he could've waited," someone said.

Ox went on, "and she went with him to the hut. It was quite dark, so he made a small light in the lantern."

"Have you left your underthings off?" he asked her.

Ray had heard enough. He spat vigorously.

"That's rubbish. I could do better than that." He stubbed his fag out on the ground and started juggling the football with both feet, a signal that it was time for another kick about.

On the way home Ray announced that he wouldn't be around for a couple of days as he had got a summer job at Slaney's printing works, just down from the Acre on Festus Street, and would be busy. Ray didn't seem too keen on the job.

"It's mainly laying out death notices, birth announcements and stuff like that. Boring, but my mum needs the money," he said.

A few days later when I got to the shed there was a degree of excitement. There, in a cardboard box, was a stack of A5 booklets entitled the 'Lion Tamer and the Doctor's Wife' written by someone called RH Lofthouse. The name seemed oddly familiar.

The story line was quite straightforward.

After a lion escapes from Hucknall Zoo Bellows, the lion tamer, tracks it down to Thieves Wood where it is savaging the doctor's wife. Fortunately, it has only managed to get as far as tearing her outer garments when Bellows steps in and, despite almost falling over his loins, ends up in a rather compromising position. The story was only somewhat spoilt by the accidental insertion of two obituary notices on the second page before it culminated in a torrid finale at the back of the shed in a local park, the description of which seemed to be quite similar to the version that Ox had read the other day.

"And she went with him to the shed. It was quite dark, so he used some Jettex fuel to start a fire using some twigs and copy of the Evening Post."

"Have you got any underpants on?" she asked him. "Yes," he answered proudly and showed her his brand-new Y fronts.

There then followed some exhausting gymnastics which ended up with them getting tangled up in the goal nets and falling asleep, only to be woken hours later by the whistle of the early-morning fish train from Grimsby.

The booklets, it seemed, had enjoyed a wide circulation. Fifty copies had been found in the library, and piles had been left on the counters of various newsagents. The Badger Box, the Nag's Head and the Shoulder of Mutton had also received their fair share. Rumour was rife, but no one seemed to know the identity of the author because, whoever 'RH Lofthouse' was, he was being much more cautious than the lion tamer.

Ray turned up late for football on Saturday carrying a large cardboard box on the crossbar of his bike. He had volunteered for an extra shift while Mr Slaney was away picking up printing supplies. I remember his hands were thick with ink and – wearing a pair of filthy dungarees, drawing on a fag and balling up the occasional clot of phlegm – he looked and sounded like a real adult.

A new wave of pamphlets containing more details of the lion tamer's amorous activities hit the streets on Monday morning. It seemed that almost every house on the Kingsway estate had been targeted. Ox had one, and we were avidly reading it in the shed when we saw a rather portly policeman walking towards us. If we hadn't guessed already, the pamphlet gave an insight into Kirkby's biggest literary mystery.

Emblazoned across the back page in large bold type was the headline:

MEET THE AUTHOR
RAY'S SHAGGING SHED
THE ACRE
KIRKBY PARK

We hardly had time to finish reading the pamphlet before the copper arrived. He seized it and put it into a large bag that already was quite full. I remember him looking around and asking the question that dare not speak its name.

"Is this, err, Ray's, err ,shagging shed?"

"No," I replied, "that's it over there," and pointed to a building a couple of hundred yards away, near the bowling green.

"Do any of you know someone called RH Lofthouse?"

John Rabbit suggested that Mr Lofthouse might be the captain of the bowls club. The copper made a note in a small black book, looked at us suspiciously and went on his way.

Rumour has it that he was later seen at Slaney's print works. Ray left his summer job soon after this and, as far as I know, never published anything else.

Today there is a blue plaque on the house where DH Lawrence was born, just a couple of miles from our shed. I don't have any of his books. Ray's birthplace has no such plaque, but somewhere I still have a treasured copy of his steamy romance and, in my heart, I know who was the better author.

Chapter 6:
Flying

Picture this. Jim Vardy's barber's shop, Prospect Street, Kirkby in Ashfield. It's late spring 1957. The floor is covered in human hair and the air is thick with the odour of Park Drive and Woodbines. On the wall there are pictures of footballers. One shows Stanley Mathews pulling on a Craven A. The caption reads, 'Cool, clean smoking, the sportsman's cigarette'. Everything is in black and white – possibly with a varnish of yellow nicotine

There are about eight customers, but no problem. Each haircut takes only about three or four minutes, unless, of course, they want to pay an extra threepence to have it singed afterwards with a wax taper, in which case it takes a bit longer.

There's no discussion of hairstyles. It's just, "The usual," or "A trim".

In later life I come to judge hairdressers by their own hairstyles, and feel that this is a good rule of thumb, so when I tell you that Jim Vardy's hair was a cross between that of Norman Deeley, the Wolverhampton Wanderers right winger, and Adolf Eichman, you will get a flavour of the service provided – even if you have never seen a photograph of either.

Sitting next to me, waiting for a haircut is John Rabbit. We are both seven years old.

A new television channel has just been launched. Before that there had just been the BBC and, although it was exciting four years earlier when we got our first television, all it seemed to have these days for kids was 'Watch with Mother' and then long interludes where there were no programmes, just lots of fill-in films showing a bloke working with clay on a potter's wheel, or speeded-up clips of trains running between London and Brighton – great the first few times you saw them, but after a while the novelty definitely faded.

In the early evening there'd be lots of boring shows like 'What's my line?' with such luminaries as Lady Isobel Barnett or Philip Harbin. Philip Harbin was television's first celebrity chef. I think only remember him because of something John had said to me.

"Jonathan, what's the difference between Philip Harbin and a cross country runner?"

I said, "I don't know."

He said, "Well, one's a pant in the country and the other is a .... in the pantry."

I thought, "What a great story," but when I told my mum she didn't seem very impressed.

It was while we waiting for our haircuts that John told me that his family had got this new-fangled thing, 'Commercial' television. Now, this was later called ITV, but in its first few months it was 'Commercial' TV because it had commercials which very quickly we called adverts. Its key selling point for me was a programme that John raved on about: 'Superman'.

John told me that Superman could actually fly and he'd do other amazing things: he could hold up bridges, lift up cars. In a word, he was fantastic.

I must admit I didn't really believe it. I mean, how could a bloke fly on television? It was impossible, but I soon found out that other kids also had this Commercial TV and they all insisted that John was telling the truth.

So me and my brother Richard started badgering my mum day and night to get a new telly. We were desperate to see Superman flying to the rescue.

I guess our campaign was quite successful because a few weeks later, a new set arrived. It was great. Sure enough it had two channels, BBC and Commercial.

I remember the first episode of Superman. Sproncing onto the screen comes this guy in tights and swimming trunks. He didn't have a six-pack, he sort of had a one-pack, and, if truth be told, he was actually a bit portly. But bloody hell, he'd run and take off and fly through the air. He was quickly up to all sorts.

I remember, in the first episode we saw, there was a train hurtling towards disaster. The track was broken and, although Superman was up in the air and miles away, he used his x-ray vision, focussed it on the broken rail and welded it so that it was fixed. Then he dived straight through the wall of a building where his x-ray vision had seen some folks robbing a bank, and arrested the lot of them. Then he lifted up a car to save a young child who was trapped underneath and generally accomplished a whole shedload of good things – all within the space of half an hour.

Superman had given me an idea, I really wanted to learn to fly. Now, I wasn't stupid or anything, but I really thought that with a bit of practice I might be able to fly off the roof of our house. I thought about it and figured it might be best to do this in stages. So first of all, I climbed up on the coal house

It was about ten feet high. I jumped off that and landed on the concrete below and it wasn't very pleasant. To be honest, it hurt. Nevertheless, I didn't give up. I tried it a couple more times before it dawned on me that if I climbed right up to the roof and jumped off that was probably gonna hurt a lot more, so I figured I needed a plan B.

I rooted around and, in the coal house, found a length of rope which must have been an old clothesline. As soon as I saw it I began figuring things out. I looked at the back garden and there was an apple tree. In an instant I had my new plan, one of almost lethal simplicity.

I climbed up the apple tree and lashed one end of the rope around a branch and began experimenting. I lowered the rope so it was about six feet off the ground, and put a loop in it. I thought a slip knot would be good because that would make it nice and snug. Feeling excited I put my head through, put my arms through, sat on a branch and launched myself into space. Almost immediately I realised that I had made a big mistake. The rope suddenly tightened around my chest and I couldn't breathe, and then it jumped and slipped under my armpits and was even tighter.

The pressure inside my chest was just enormous. I couldn't breathe. My head felt as though it was about to explode. And my feet were kicking, kicking like crazy trying to get purchase on the branches of the tree but they couldn't. I was swinging backwards and forwards and then slowly round and round and, as I swung round, I could see into the house and there was my mum in the kitchen. I could see her through the kitchen window and the next thing she's out of the back door and there's something flashing in her hand. She has a knife and, I kid you not, she touched the rope and it exploded. I fell to the ground and in an instant my mum was cutting the rope from around my middle and picking me up in her arms.

That episode was a milestone in my life. It told me a number of things. Apart from the realisation that my mum was much more reliable than Superman, it taught me that too much telly can be bad for young kids; it also taught me that sometimes our lives hang by a thread and, finally, it taught me that flying isn't really all that it's cracked up to be.

Chapter 7:
Sadomasochism

I guess I must have been about seven and a half years old when I discovered sadomasochism.

And I'll tell you how it happened.

Now, words are a peculiar thing, sometimes you hear them and you know immediately what they mean. For example, when my grandmother used to threaten to "tan my hide," I knew exactly what she meant.

"I'll tan your flaming hide," or "I'll tan your bloody hide," and I'd run as she chased me with a length of cane. So, I knew that to get tanned meant being thrashed with a stick. But there were other words that I didn't understand, and by the time I was seven I was quite adept at looking these up in the dictionary. In fact, I had quite a vocabulary.

It was interesting that when I went to junior school there was a girl in our class whose name was actually Tanya Hyde but her surname was spelt with an y instead of an i. I often wondered if her middle name was bloody, but I never did find out.

Anyway, back to sadomasochism.

It was early summer. My sister came back from school one day in a right huff. She flung her bag into the cupboard under the stairs and stomped off muttering "Our P.E. teacher's a sadomasochist".

I thought, 'well there's a word I haven't heard before', so I went to look it up in the dictionary. I can't remember exactly what it said but it was something like this….

'One who takes pleasure from inflicting pain on themselves and others. Often of a sexual nature.'

Mmm, that's interesting, I'll file it away with those other words that I'd looked up like gonorrhoea and prostitute.

Anyway, it wasn't long after this my mum and dad's friends, Joyce and Aubrey, paid us a visit. Joyce and Aubrey weren't like most folks in Kirkby. For a start they were well off, they had a car and even more remarkably, they often went 'ABROAD.'

They'd just been on what they described as a 'motoring holiday' in the south of France, and my mum said that they'd spent a week doing nothing but getting tanned. I thought, 'hold on a minute are they sadists or are they masochists – spending all their time getting tanned?'

I thought that I'd have to find out a bit more. Anyway, when they arrived it was clear that that something serious had happened to them because their skin was totally discoloured. Aubrey looked as though he was bruised from head to foot ,and Joyce was even darker in colour, and rather than hiding this away it seemed as though they were dressed in a manner calculated to emphasise the bruising. Aubrey, I remember, was wearing a sort of pale cream-coloured linen jacket, and a white shirt and pale slacks, and light brown loafers. He topped it off with a white panama hat. It made him look even more discoloured and Joyce, well, pretty much the same.

Anyway, while my mum and dad were talking to Joyce, I decided I'd have a chat with Aubrey who was a nice chap and who'd always talk to you as if you were an adult. A clever bloke.

So, I said to him, "Aubrey, you've been getting tanned all week?"

He said "Yes Jonathan, yes, yes."

I said "Does it hurt?"

He laughed. He said "Well, it can do at first

So I said "What do you do about that?"

He said, "Well I get Joyce to rub some Nivea cream on or maybe some oil, but you know sometimes you can get blisters to begin with and then you have to lay off it for a couple of days."

I thought, Christ, he's quite open about this.

I said "and, er, whereabouts do you get tanned?"

He said "Antibes"

Antibes sounded like a medical term, you know, something like vertebra or oesophagus, the sort of word you'd get on Emergency Ward 10 on the television.

I didn't have my dictionary to hand, but thought 'Mm, I'll look that up later.'

I figured, well, he's either been hitting himself in the Antibes or getting Joyce to do it for him, and I was wondering quite where he was hitting her.

So, I said to him, "What about Joyce?"

He said, "Well it was great for Joyce. She really loved it. In fact, it's done wonders for her sciatica."

Sciatica was another word I didn't know. But it seemed to me that it was probably another medical term, and I figured out it was probably something like that word 'syphilis' that I'd seen in the dictionary.

So, what they've done, they've gone on holiday, they've done some sadomasochism and it's helped cure Joyce's syphilis.

I thought, that's fascinating. They are certainly interesting people.

Anyway, after they'd gone I thought, 'I'm not really sure about all of this so I'd better check out with my mum.'

My mum was having what she called 'a quiet five minutes.' She didn't often have a 'a quiet five minutes' because she had six kids. but there she was, sitting in an arm chair in the living room, reading a book. She loved reading.

I could tell she was rapt in concentration because she had a cigarette in her right hand suspended in mid-air with about an inch and a half of ash hanging off of it. She plainly hadn't moved for some minutes.

I said to mum, "Can I ask you a question?"

"Yeah," she said, still not moving.

I said, "Are Joyce and Aubrey sadomasochists?"

She looked at me and said, "Why?"

I said, "Well, they've been tanning themselves for a week in the south of France, and it sounds as though it was really painful."

She laughed. The ash dropped off her cigarette, she took a drag and said, "Yeah, I suppose they must be."

I was satisfied. I thought to myself, 'well, that's enough learning for one day.'

So, I went outside in the back garden. The sun was still shining. I opened my copy of the Beezer and started to read and, in five minutes, with the heat of the sun and all the knowledge I'd accumulated, I was fast asleep.

I just hoped that I wouldn't get burnt.

Chapter 8:
Sandwiches

I must admit that I've never really been a fan of sandwiches. I can't remember where my distaste for them comes from, but I think it might about something to do with the potted meat sandwiches which were trotted out regularly on Sunday afternoons at my grandmother's house.

I remember looking at them and thinking, 'Christ, how could you eat that muck?'

Anyway, most people seemed to enjoy them, and sandwiches would appear from time to time. I remember when my brother Richard started working for Raleigh in Nottingham. It was miles away and involved a bus and a train journey, and required him to get up for work almost before he went to bed.

My dad got into the habit of making him sandwiches to take to work; they were 'salad dressing' sandwiches. To this day, my brother can't think about them without wanting to throw up. I thought they looked revolting and were vaguely reminiscent of something that you might regurgitate after a bad night out at the Nag's Head.

Anyway, my younger brother Nick started working at Newstead Colliery when he was 15. His job interview was quite interesting.

My dad, who was a Freemason, was eager to give him some secret tips and he told Nick, "When you go for interview, if they ask you if you have any other names you must say 'yes' and tell that this other name is Lewis." Nick looked puzzled.

"Why should I do that?"

My dad said, "It's a secret sign, it will let them know that you're a member of the Freemason fraternity and you'll get the job."

Now this might have worked well if Nick had been going for a job at Barclays bank on Station Street, or even a clerical job at Bray's toyshop on Low Moor Road, but at Newstead Colliery nobody needed a secret codename to get a job because this was 1965 and jobs were ten a penny. Industry was crying out for people, and even my older brother Richard – although he had been sacked from a few – had managed to get four or five jobs without too much trouble.

I remember the day of Nick's interview, he told me that he had been ushered into a small room and given a form to complete. The selection process seemed to be straightforward: fill in your name, age, date of birth and address and start next Monday. Basically it was: if you are alive you've got the job.

They had to go through the motions however, so Nick was asked a few perfunctory questions. The most difficult, Nick recalled, was "Why do you want to work at Newstead Colliery?"

Nick didn't really have an answer for this, I mean, who would have an answer? Never mind, that didn't seem to worry the bloke the other side of the desk.

The difficulty came when the interviewer started to go through Nick's application form. When he got to the section where Nick had filled in his Christian name and surname he asked, "Have you got any other names?"

It had all been going so swimmingly up to this point, and Nick was not quite sure how to answer. He paused for a moment and answered, "Sort of." The interviewer looked puzzled.

"What do you mean, sort of?"

Nick was embarrassed, and I guess he went into panic mode. "Well, I've sort of got another name. It's... secret."

"What do you mean, it's secret?"

Nick decided to go the whole hog. "It's Lewis," he muttered and flashed a conspiratorial smile.

"Lewis?"

"Yeah"

"Well it's not what it says on your birth certificate."

Nick said, "No, I told you already, it's secret."

The interviewer shifted uncomfortably, and Nick said that there was a rather ambiguous tension between them for a minute.

It took quite a few minutes for the interviewer to regain his composure, and I'm not surprised. I don't think he'd ever had an applicant for Newstead Colliery with a secret name.

I'm not sure what happened in the rest of the interview, but I do know that when Nick came home he was not best pleased. The front door slammed and he stormed into the kitchen and swore at my dad.

Now, nobody ever swore at my dad, but Nick did on this day. He used the 'F' word, a word you'd never hear in our household.

He said, "What the fucking hell are you doing telling me to use that name, Lewis? The bloke down at Bentick thinks I'm an absolute bloody idiot. I looked like I didn't even know me own fucking name."

My dad couldn't placate him, and Nick stormed off upstairs. Despite all of this Nick did get the job, and this leads us back to the issue of sandwiches.

One thing you need to know about my dad was that he was really gentle, a lovely guy, and really looked after us kids. He took pleasure in making sandwiches for us if we were going anywhere. He knew I didn't like sandwiches, so I was out of the firing line, but Nick and Richard sometimes had sandwiches imposed on them. Nick quite liked it because he managed to reach an accommodation with my dad. Nick would usually only have cheese sandwiches, and he knew that my dad couldn't ruin them.

I remember one famous day, however. We must have run out of cheese. Nick was sitting in front of the telly before heading off on night shift. My dad asked Nick what he wanted in his snap tin.

Now, when you are working down the pit you consume a lot of calories and everyone would make sure that they had plenty of high-protein, high-carbohydrate food. You know the sort of thing, cheese, a big piece of cake and some fruit. I remember on this particular day, my dad saying to Nick, "Do you want pork pie or sandwiches?" and Nick saying "Yes," absentmindedly. He was watching Thunderbirds or something on the telly.

When Nick came home the next morning, again he went absolutely bananas.

He said to my dad, "What the hell did you put in my sandwich tin?"

And my dad said, "Pork pie sandwiches."

Nick looked at him. He said, "Have you ever tried eating pork pie sandwiches? It's like eating a cardboard box. It's inedible. The people at work – no one wanted any; I couldn't even swap any of it."

My dad looked at him. "Well I asked you if you wanted pork pie or sandwiches and you said 'yes', so I thought I'd make you a pork pie sandwich."

Nick wasn't impressed and after that he started making his own sandwiches, which I think was what we later called a 'win-win' scenario, but I remember that not long after he again came back from work in a really black mood.

He said, "Some bastard's been stealing my snap."

Now, Nick worked with a gang of folks down near the coal face. It was filthy and dangerous work, but comradeship was everything. There was an unwritten law. Each man depended on the next, and mutual trust was an absolute necessity. Lives depended on it.

But on this occasion, somebody had broken the bond of trust. There had been a spate of thefts from within the team. There was a pattern to the thefts – food. People would find an apple had gone missing, or a piece of cake, but the most frequent target of the thief was sandwiches.

Now this had happened to Nick and, although he was young, he was the sort of character you wouldn't want to tangle with. He was ferociously strong, a real street fighter, and people were frightened of him. He had the honour of having his own pit horse and he used to ride it down to the coal face. He was quite a man about the pit to be honest.

He told me how he used to wake his horse up. He said that if his pit horse was lying on the floor asleep, there was a technique he'd use which I don't think you would find in many equestrian guides. It was called 'Wazzing in its tab'. He told me that you could kick the pit horse and prod it and cajole it, but, believe it or don't, Nick assured me that the only thing that worked was to piss in its earhole.

Now Nick had this off pat, so that after the first few drops the horse would jump up, shake its head and trot off as happy as Larry. By the way, once a year the horse would come out for a week and graze in the fields above ground while the local schoolchildren fed him apples and sugar lumps. Remarkably, despite the almost constant risk of urinary infections, his horse lasted many years.

Anyway, to get back to the sandwiches, Nick figured that he'd lay a trap for the sandwich thief. One day he took potted meat, foul-smelling stuff that looked awful, and sure enough his sandwiches got taken. Nick noticed another pattern, the thief liked potted meat, so this is how the trap worked.

On this particular day, Nick took two slices of bread and butter and he got some droppings from his horse's stable and spread the sandwiches with them, wrapped them up in greaseproof paper and let it be known that he'd got potted meat sandwiches for lunch.

At snap time all the gang sat down on pieces of old conveyor belt.

Nick said to the assembled group, "Somebody's been stealing my sandwiches, and today they think they've got potted meat, but they haven't. Actually, it's horse shit. So, you are all going to take out your snap and eat it here, right now, and if I find who has been stealing I'll kill 'em."

He watched. To one side, one of his work mates was almost gagging over his food, but he ate it.

Nick and his mates never had a problem with sandwiches again.

So, whenever I'm searching for a quick bite to eat, you'll never find me at the sandwich counter. In fact, whenever I see folks filling their cheeks with the latest off-the-shelf offering I find myself still wondering just what exactly is mixed up in all that gelatinous gloop that seems to be slormed all over most of them, but then again, perhaps its best that I never find out.

Chapter 9:
Divine Retribution

When I was eleven years old, I had the good fortune to gain a place at a prestigious grammar school about five miles away from Kirkby. Established in the mid 1500s, it had all the trappings of schoolboy yarns complete with quadrangles, bell towers, science labs and an oak-panelled school hall with the names of long-dead headmasters and old boys written in gold paint on the honours boards around its walls.

For a long time I had no idea how the school worked. Subjects that I had been really good at in my primary school now became a problem. In English, for example, we seemed to spend all of our time drawing boxes and doing something perplexing called clause analysis. To this day I have no idea what the hell all this was about.

If English was bad, French was even worse. Our teacher tried to instil in us the importance of being able to say such useful things as, 'where is the window?' and 'the ceiling is white', before moving on to more complex conversational gambits including 'the cat is on the table' and 'I have two arms'.

French vocabulary was a mystery. Why, for Christ's sake, did they have to use some arty-farty word like 'fenetre' when plain old 'window', perhaps with a French accent, would be just as good, if not better?

French and English, however, were a breeze in comparison with mathematics. Our teacher, a bald man called Gammond ,was committed to the pleasures of factorisation and sadism.

I think he must have had an honours degree in violence ,and he manifested an especial hatred of anyone who could not manipulate simultaneous equations.

Despite my fear of him, somehow, during the first term, I seemed to do quite well. I understood everything and, although my homework marks were moderate, I was quite happy with my progress.

The turning point came at Christmas time. We had end-of-term exams in every subject. I performed spectacularly poorly in most areas. The only exception was religious education, which was ironic because I was already beginning to doubt the existence of God. Curiously, one reason for my success was that I was the only person who knew the correct name for the most desperate tribe of the Israelites; this was mainly because I was an avid reader of the Desperate Dan strip in the 'Dandy'.

The final grading system worked like this. The marks for each subject were added up, and each student's total was entered on a chart at the front of the classroom. The boy with the highest total marks was top of the class, and the boy with the lowest marks was bottom of the class. As the results came in, marks were added on a daily basis.

Finally, only the maths result was missing and I knew I probably needed a good score in order to avoid finishing bottom of the entire class. My main competitor for this dubious honour was McGrady, who seemed even more out of touch with what was going on than I was. Still, I knew it would be a near-run thing.

I'll never forget that maths lesson. We all waited. I was feeling confident because I knew that I had many of the same answers as the brightest boys in the class, and I expected to be within the top half dozen.

I heard Mr Gammond walking upstairs and along the corridor. He came in, a pile of papers in his hands, stood at the front of the room, and began reading the marks in descending order.

"Green, ninety-six percent; Fells, ninety-three percent; Higham, eighty-seven percent; and so on.

Soon the marks were down to fifty percent and I began to feel a bit concerned.

"Klapkowski, forty-eight percent; Hill, forty-four percent,;Franks, thirty-nine percent."

I was now getting worried as the roll call of names continued and the marks became lower and lower. My head began to spin, and I felt distinctly unwell. I thought I was going to be sick. This was a bad dream.

Now there was only a handful of papers left.

"Gobey, twenty-one percent; McGrady, fourteen percent;" and then, finally, me, "Evans, eight percent."

I was in shock. I couldn't believe it. Surely there was some mistake. I put my hand up.

"Please sir, can I have a look at my paper?"

Mr Gammond turned red. "Come here Evans."

I walked to the front of the class and could see that there was only one sheet of my answer papers and I had written several pages.

"There's only one page" I blurted out. "Where are the rest of them?"

Before I could say anything else, Mr Gammond hit me hard across my cheek with all his force and sent me flying across the room He then picked up all of the papers and tore them to shreds destroying any evidence that there may have been.

I returned to my desk and sat down burning with anger and shame and vowed that one day, somehow, I would get my revenge.

I didn't finish quite bottom of the class that term. My knowledge of the tribe of Dan enabled me to finish two marks above McGrady, a fact which, for a short time, restored my fading belief in a divine being.

My revenge came a year later, in the early spring of 1963. The school was scheduled to have a government inspection. By this time I had been placed in the lowest class in year two –

comprised of those pupils who had done most poorly in the first year.

As things turned out, it was unfortunate for Mr Gammond that this inspection took place during the winter of what later became known as the mini ice age.

The ground was frozen for months on end and my main passion, football, was interrupted. Had it not been for this fact, things may have played out differently. As it was, Mr Gammond was due to give a model lesson to our class on the day after a rearranged FA Cup tie which I was going to go to see no matter what.

In preparation for his lesson, Mr Gammond gave the whole class a very long and difficult algebra exercise to complete. I realised that I could not both do the exercise and go to the football match, so I decided very quickly to simply make up all my answers to the questions that had been set. During the morning break I therefore scribbled down responses to each of the sixty questions we had been given.

I'll give you a couple of examples.

"Q 1. Two oranges, three bananas and four apples cost one shilling and three pence . Three oranges, two bananas, and one apple cost ten pence . How many oranges can you buy for two shillings?

I had no idea, so I wrote down the first number that came into my head – fifteen and seven eighths.

Question 2 was similar:

Q2. Four apples and two oranges cost two shillings and sixpence and one apple and three oranges cost one shilling and threepence. How much does each apple and each orange cost?

Again, I took a guess based on what I felt was likely – based on what I'd seen at the greengrocers.

I answered "apples are threepence and oranges eightpence ha'penny."

I quickly got into my stride and by the end of break had answers to all of the questions.

I was just putting my book away when Ivan Franks, one of my best friends, noticed what I was doing.

"Have you done your maths homework?" he asked.

I hesitated. I didn't want to give him the wrong answers and get him into trouble, but then the thought came to me that if we both had wrong answers it would deflect some of the attention away from me so, with only a little reluctance, I let him copy my work.

If that was as far as things had gone then it would probably have been okay for Mr. Gammond, but at lunchtime I noticed Peter Foster and Bob Clarke were also copying my homework.

Then Pete North got hold of it and, by the end of lunchtime, it had spread like a virus. What really worried me was when Robert Pearce, the class maths guru, also copied it. I knew then that things had really got out of hand and that the shit would hit the fan the next day.

What I needed was a new plan. I admitted to Ivan Franks that all my answers were rubbish and we both had to change our work otherwise we would be in big trouble. He refused to believe me.

His logic was sound – "Robert Pearce has got the same answers so they must be right."

I tried hard to persuade him otherwise, but it was no good. So, I just looked after my own interests. I ripped the offending answers out of my exercise book and, on the bus home, invented sixty completely new answers.

That night I went to the cup tie and I enjoyed it immensely.

The next day all of the pupils handed in their work before the beginning of school. Our maths lesson was scheduled for the last period of the day and Mr. Gammond, observed by the government inspector, planned to go through our homework and showcase the impact of his excellent teaching on the work of his grammar school students.

Looking back, I'm quite surprised how calm I felt that afternoon. I remember Mr. Gammond striding into the room carrying our exercise books, followed by an elderly gentleman in a pinstripe suit. We all stood up as they entered.

"Sit down boys," Mr Gammond snarled. He looked rather unwell. In later life I would've said it looked as though he was about to have a stroke but, at the time, I just thought he looked rather flushed.

"Now, let's look at the homework."

He walked around the class handing the exercise books out. He then read out the first question.

"Class. Two oranges, three bananas and four apples cost one shilling and three pence. Three oranges, two bananas, and one apple cost ten pence. How many oranges can you buy for two shillings?"

"Pearce, what was your answer?"

Pearce looked pleased with himself. As the best mathematician in the class he was often asked to explain solutions to dullards like me.

"Fifteen and seven eighths sir," came the confident reply,

"Pearce, stand up." Pearce rose to his feet, looking pleased with himself, certain that he had got the right answer.

"Tell me Pearce, how did you solve the problem?" Pearce, who had flaming red hair, suddenly looked as though he was about to spontaneously combust.

There was a very uncomfortable pause.

"I don't know sir."

"DON'T KNOW?" Mr. Gammond roared. "What was it, divine intervention? Who else got the same answer?"

Twenty eight other boys stood up. Pearce had now become a human chameleon and had turned a nasty shade of grey.

"Clarke, how did you get this answer?"

Clarke mumbled something.

"WHAT? Speak up lad."

Clarke looked at the floor. I think he was waiting for it to swallow him up and get him out of this awful situation. He looked desperately around to his classmates for help, but almost everyone else seemed to be looking for the same exit as he was.

There was another long and painful pause as Mr Gammond walked around the class eyeballing several pupils at uncomfortably close quarters. He composed himself with some difficulty.

"Right, question two. Franks, what was your answer?"

"Apples are threepence and oranges eightpence ha'penny, sir" came the reply.

Mr. Gammond glowered. "Who else got the same answer?" Twenty eight hands rose slowly into the air.

There was further interrogation. How, he demanded had everyone got the same answers and all of them wildly, implausibly incorrect? In fact, so wrong that one question elicited an answer of "fifteen coconuts" in answer to the question 'How many cabbages can be bought for the same price as X oranges?'

It went on like this for about fifteen minutes, and then Mr. Gammond did what I like to call his 'Hitler impersonation.' He screamed, yelled and flung his hands around as though he were speaking at a rally in the Berlin Sportpalast whilst simultaneously trying to catch hold of an invisible trapeze.

He raved about honesty, diligence and hard work, and then handed out detentions and extra work to everyone apart from me. I was singled out for special mention.

"Evans, stand up," he said.

Ivan Franks was giving me an odd look – a sort of combination of admiration, disbelief and loathing. This is it, I thought, somehow, he has discovered that I'm to blame. I stood in a world of my own and waited for the axe to fall.

"Evans, you got four of the questions right. Can you tell the class how you got the answer to question eleven?"

I was astonished so I answered honestly. "I just guessed it sir."

Mr. Gammond raised his eyes heavenward. He breathed in deeply. He then said something that has stayed with me for all these years.

"Boys, look at Evans. He may be an idiot but at least he's honest."

I don't recall how the lesson ended but, shortly after the government inspection was completed, Mr. Gammond apparently got a new job elsewhere at very short notice and we never saw him again.

By the way, my team won the Cup tie 4-3 with a last-minute goal. That night I went to bed happy, a big smile on my face, feeling that all was well with the world and that, after all, just maybe, there was a god.

Chapter 10:
The Cup Final Ticket

I don't know whether you've ever seen those Chix famous footballer cards, but I'm thinking in particular of the one of Tommy Lawton. He was the England centre forward whom Notts County signed for a world-record fee in 1949. There he is, a northern lad in his England shirt, arms folded, three lions on his chest; staring out at the world, his jet black hair combed straight back with an immaculate centre parting.

My Uncle Ted had modelled his hairstyle on Tommy Lawton's.

"It's like polished brass," he used to say proudly.

He maintained that he had no need to use Brylcream or Silvikrin to keep it in place, as his scalp produced its own natural oils. Indeed, he swore that he had not washed his hair for more than 40 years, and saw no need to do so.

Bodily hygiene wasn't the only unusual thing about Uncle Ted: viewed from the front his face always reminded me of a sharpened pencil. He had a sort of feral look and I remember me grandma saying in a not-very-quiet voice that, "He looks as though his mother's been run wi' a rat."

Now, I'd heard at school about people speaking in tongues and I figured that this was what my grandmother was doing, and while I couldn't translate this expression exactly, somehow I knew what she meant.

If my grandmother sometimes spoke in tongues, Uncle Ted was an expert in the field. A typical conversation might go like this:

Ted might ask, "Have you seen him?"

"Who?"

"HIM, you know , Doings. You know, with the wottsit. He lives at errr, where is it? You know, with thingy."

I didn't join up the dots at the time , but the fact that Ted was often seen dancing home from Sterland's club late at night and had a deserved reputation as the champion Guinness drinker of Kirkby may have had something to do with his linguistic prowess.

Ted's one redeeming feature was he was mad keen on football and was the proud possessor of a season ticket at Nottingham Forest. He had been going to see them since the year dot and in all that time the only honour they ever won was the championship of the third division (north) in about 1951. 1959, however, was destined to be different.

It all started quite inauspiciously. It was a Saturday afternoon in the first week of January. Frost was hard on the ground and the football pitches on Kirkby Acre were like iron. It didn't stop us, in fact nothing would stop us playing football.

Even when it snowed, we would trample the pitch flat and still play. That's what you did in those days.

It was some time after about three o' clock when Ivan Franks turned up with the news that, "Forest are losing two-nil at half time to Tooting and Mitcham".

This was a bit of a shock because Tooting and Mitcham were an amateur team and Forest were in the first division; and the thought of them losing to these no-hopers, in the FA Cup, of all things, was beyond belief. As it happened, Forest managed to scramble a draw courtesy of an own goal and a dubious penalty, and then progressed to the next round of the Cup, which they sailed through without too much difficulty.

Excitement was beginning to mount when they played arch-rivals Birmingham City in the next round, and I remember being in Jim Vardy's barber's shop as, after an epic series of replays, I heard on the radio that Forest had eventually won through. A couple of week later they put out the Cup-holders Bolton Wanderers – Nat Lofthouse, the Lion of Vienna and all – in the quarter finals.

Semi-final day was a day of high tension, and I think everybody in Kirkby must have been glued to the BBC sports service as Johnny Quigley scored twenty minutes from the end to send the local heroes to the Cup Final for the first time since the 1890s.

At school, excitement was at fever pitch; every kid it seemed wanted a Forest outfit and, amongst adults, rumours abounded about Cup Final tickets.

About a month before the big game, Uncle Ted came round to visit. This was quite unusual. I think he had been in training for defence of his Guinness drinking title in the Badger Box and he seemed in an especially good mood.

"Jonathan, come and sit on me wottsit."

He patted his knee.

"I've got a surprise for you."

I was intrigued. Uncle Ted wasn't famed for surprises.

"How would you like to go to the doings, you know to see IT?"

"To see what?" I asked

"You know, IT, the thingumajig, you know against … THEM?"

I looked at my mum for help , but she was none the wiser.

"I'm getting one, and I'm getting one for you as well."

He started jiggling his knee and humming a weird tune, something like the Dambusters' theme, "Pom, pom pom pompompom pom pompom pom, pom pompmpom pom."

"I'm getting you a Cup Final ticket."

A Cup Final ticket! Wow! That was incredible. It was going to be the trip of a lifetime. We would get the bus to Nottingham station and catch the football special to London, then travel by something called The Underground, and then by bus to the match.

That night I was so excited that I could barely sleep. Over and over in my mind I imagined the journey and the big game, and could hardly wait to tell my friends.

At school the news travelled quickly. I'm certain that I was the only kid who had a ticket. The game seemed to be the only topic of conversation. Even the teachers mentioned it in class ,and it was never off the pages of the local and national press.

Tickets were like gold dust and there was huge excitement when, two weeks before the final, the Nottingham Evening Post announced it had obtained eight tickets and would be holding a raffle for them. To enter, all you had to do was buy a copy of the paper, fill out a coupon and post it in.

The draw was held a few days later and a young lad, David, who lived just down the road, incredibly won one of the tickets. This seemed like a miracle, all the more so because David's birthday was the same as mine and we both travelled to matches on the local supporters' bus.

Time dragged, but eventually Cup Final week arrived. Clive Kirk told me that Purdey's newsagents had copies of the match programme, and I remember buying one for a shilling. Later the same day I bought a red and white rosette from Edgar Coats gents' outfitters on Kingsway where the store was covered in red and white bunting. By now I was so excited I could hardly contain myself.

On the Wednesday before the game, however, the bombshell

landed, I had been making enquiries from my auntie about travel arrangements when, after tea, my mum took me to one side and said she wanted a chat with me. In the lounge she sat me down and told me the awful truth. My Uncle Ted had just owned up to the fact that he hadn't got me a ticket after all.

My mum couldn't explain why, but straight away I figured that he probably didn't even try to get me one. I realised instinctively that he was the sort of grown up who believed that kids were unimportant, and that whatever was said to them counted for nothing. In retrospect, I figure that, in all probability, he didn't even remember making the promise.

I can't recall my immediate reaction but I know that I was terribly upset. My brother Richard put his arms round me, looked me in the eye and said

"Don't worry. Next time Forest get to the Cup Final I'll get you a ticket. I promise."

I was really touched especially as Richard had no interest whatsoever in football, and I immediately felt a bit better, because I knew that he was always as good as his word.

If I was having it tough, David was having it even worse. Despite him winning a lucky ticket, his father wouldn't allow him to go to the game. Instead he placed an advertisement in the local paper offering the ticket for sale. It was sold within hours. Years later I actually met the man who bought it – a complete stranger – but that is another story.

The beauty of childhood is that pain and upset never last

long, and watching the match on the TV could not have been more exciting, especially as Forest won the game.

Year after year, Forest tried to reach the Cup Final again. Several times they came tantalisingly close, but it wasn't until more than 30 years later than they manged to do so. I tried desperately to get a ticket, but again I had no luck, so I resigned myself to watching it at home. On the Thursday before the game I arrived back in the early evening to hear the phone ringing off the hook. I picked it up. It was my brother Richard and I'll never forget what he said.

"Do you remember that promise I made to you?"

"What promise?"

"You know, in 1959."

The memories came flooding back

"I've got you a ticket, in fact I've got one for me as well."

How he managed to do this is something I won't go into here, but two days later we found ourselves, hours before kick off, drinking in the atmosphere outside the stadium. With a lump in my throat I saw the Kirkby supporters' bus arrive, the same people that I used to travel with when I was a child and then, as we awaited the arrival of the team coaches, I heard a yell from across the road:

"Jonathan"

I looked up. There he was, older certainly, a bit thin on top. It was David with a young child – his son. Yes, we'd both finally got there. Thirty years later than we had planned , but as they say, it was better late than never.

Chapter 11:
Trainspotting

'Unmitigated England'
Came swinging down the line
That day the February sun
Did crisp and crystal shine.
Dark red at Kirkby Bentinck stood
A steeply gabled farm
'Mid ash trees and a sycamore
In charismatic calm.
A village street – a manor house –
A church – then, tally ho!
We pounded through a housing scheme
With tellymasts a-row,
Where cars of parked executives
Did regimented wait
Beside administrative blocks
Within the factory gate.

John Betjeman

I have never really been a fan of trainspotting and, since I left Kirkby, I don't think that I have ever met anyone who was.

Now don't get me wrong, I like trains and I've been on some great railway journeys: the Darjeeling mail, the Mumbai

Express from Trivandrum; along the Nile from Cairo to Aswan, through the wilds of the Sudan from Khartoum to Kosti, the Overlander across Southern Australia; the Meshed to Teheran line across the Dasht-e Kavir; and from Mandalay to Rangoon. I've slept on floors, on luggage racks and, on one famous occasion, got my whole family put up in the kitchen of the Kandy express.

I've been shot at and robbed, been derailed, met smugglers and thieves, and even fallen in love. My favourite train, though, has to be the one that we used to catch each summer from Nottingham station on the way to our annual holiday in Bognor Regis.

The whole family would wait expectantly on platform one. We heard it before we saw it, the rails would sing and the song would change into a rumble and then a roar, and from the tunnel to our right billows of smoke would emerge followed almost immediately by a magnificent steam engine.

I loved trains, and by the time I was four or five years old my mind was made up. Like most of my friends, I wanted to be an engine driver.

My love of trains has never faded, but I never became obsessed in the way that some boys did. I say boys advisedly, because I never met a girl who ever went down that track.

These boys were 'trainspotters'. They met at odd places like the loco sheds at the back of the Summit Colliery or by the level crossing on Station Street, and they carried books filled with printed numbers. These numbers identified locomotives ,and there were thousands of them. Each engine had a class number and a five-digit identifier, and this knowledge seemed to me to be more than most normal human beings would ever want or need.

One book I saw recently was for the Southern Region Railway. It was about 40 pages long and listed 400 engines per page. That's about 16,000 in total, and that is for just one region. I often wondered if these books were produced during the war to bore any invading German troops to death.

Trainspotters would religiously mark off any engine they spotted with a ruler and a blue biro. Seeing a particular engine was known as 'copping it', sometimes kids were able to get on the footplate or in the driver's cab and this was known as 'cabbing'.

I really couldn't see the point but, as I didn't want to be left out, I purchased my own notebook and sat down one night with my biro and ruler, and in next to no time had amassed an incredible collection. Being a novice, however, led to my undoing. I remember one lad looking with interest, at my book and asking the question that I was not really prepared for, "Have you got any namers?"

I had no idea what a 'namer' was. I didn't know it then, but some engines had fancy names like The Iron Duke or The Glasgow Highlander. The latter is quite odd, because even I know that Glasgow isn't in the Highlands.

I decided to take a punt and feeling quite confident said, "Yeah, two: the Milk Train and the Fish Train."

I mentioned these because they were the were only two trains that I had ever heard referred to by name. I have no idea where the Milk Train came from but the Fish Train was rumoured to come from Grimsby. Quite why they came through Kirkby is anyone's guess.

The fish train was easy to identify, because you could smell it before you saw it.

When it went past folks used to say, "There's only two things that smell like the Grimsby fish train and one of them's the Grimsby fish train."

I never really understood what this meant, but I do recall that when I told my mum this she gave me a belt round the earhole.

Anyway, my failure to give a correct listing of namers sort of gave the game away and I don't ever recall doing anymore underlinings in my trainspotter's handbook.

I do recall though one day, when I was about eleven, I was on my way home one evening when I bumped into my friend Pete Allin, who was a bit older than me. He had arranged a date and told me he was going to take this girl down the quarries.

Now, taking someone one 'down the quarries', had a number of connotations, if you get my meaning, and I admit that I felt intrigued and a little jealous, and I wondered when I would be old enough to 'go down the quarries' with someone.

We met with Pete's date by the railway crossing just down from the Acre, and I was going to continue on my way home. To Pete's dismay, however, his date had a friend with her. I had seen her once before and knew that her name was Janice. Pete seemed a bit put out by the situation but I saw the solution immediately.

"I could, err, go with Janice," I suggested hopefully. Janice smiled at her friend but didn't look directly at me.
As we were standing there a group of lads ran up and called to me.
"There's a namer at Kirkby sheds. Come on, we can cab it."

I realised in an instant that I could choose trainspotting or choose life. It didn't take me any time at all to make my mind up.

I took my new friend's hand and crossed the tracks with her towards the quarries.

Chapter 12:
The End of the
Beginning

I remember my mum once saying to me when I was on my way to school one fine spring morning. "Jonathan, one day you'll look back and think that these were the best days of your life."

I looked at her and answered, with total honesty," I already do."

I was all of five years old.

Folks say that all good things come to an end sooner or later, well I guess, in a way, they do, but the good things from my childhood are still with me, and in many ways, they have not left me.

In other ways, however, they did come to an end, and the end came in stages without me ever realising what was happening. I think it all started when I went to grammar school and got separated from many of my old mates, Clive Kirk, Michael Atherton and John Rabbitt. I never saw any of them again.

Another landmark was the day I was called to see the head teacher, Mr Boulton, a military-style gent who told me that that I was going to be expelled because my work was just not up to scratch. As he told me this my mind was in a whirl.

My parents had been so proud of me when I passed my 11-plus, and had gone to great expense kitting me out with the uniform, sports bag and leather satchel; and I couldn't help thinking how upset they would be.

I also felt incredibly embarrassed, after all, only really stupid kids got expelled, didn't they?

He told me to collect my things and go home and then, almost as an afterthought, he asked if I had anything to say for myself. I felt as though I was in the dock. I knew instinctively that what I said next was important and could change the rest of my life. My mouth was dry and then out it came, "Sorry sir," and tears welled up in my eyes. Mr Boulton turned and looked out of the window. I think he was finding this almost as difficult as me.

He cleared his throat, blew his nose and swivelled round to face me once again. "Evans I'm going to give you one last chance. If your marks don't improve next term, you will have to leave."

I walked out of his office feeling that I'd stepped away from the gallows, went back to class and waited for the holidays to begin.

When I got home, I had a letter from the school to give to my mum. When I gave it to her, her eyes shone with excitement, she put down her ironing, wiped her hands on her apron and eagerly tore open the envelope.

Looking back, I think she was expecting news that I'd been

awarded the Nobel prize or something, but as she read it, her expression changed.

She looked at me, gave me hug, and said, "Never mind, you are doing your best."

The only problem was, I knew I wasn't doing my best.

I was worried about what my dad was going to say, but mum looked at me and said, "Don't worry , I'll take care of your dad." When he came in, I heard him and my mum in the kitchen talking, and then he came and sat next to me on the settee and handed me a cup of tea. He didn't say a word.

Very soon afterwards, a friend of my brother Richard came round. I think mum had arranged it. This bloke's name was Chas Barlow, he was 16 years old and quite the funniest person I knew. Chas had just got a job doing something called computer programming. I didn't know what a computer was, and I definitely hadn't an idea what programming was either.

I went for a walk with Chas. Richard was with us, but Chas did all the talking.

"What are you going to do when you leave school, are you going to work down the pit, shovel coke at Rexco, or get a job at Wheatley's builders' merchants in Kirkby?"

None of these options really appealed to me, so I asked Chas about his job. He told me he earned a thousand quid a year, a fabulous sum for a kid of 16 – it was more that a face worker at Newstead Colliery would earn in those days. He also told me that next year his firm was going to provide him with a company car.

Chas explained in detail the advantages of a car. "What will you do at weekends when you leave school – you know, Friday and Saturday nights?"

"Go to Mansfield I guess, to the disco at the Eight Bells."

"How will you get there?"

"On the bus."

"What time's the last bus home?"

"Quarter to eleven."

"And what if you pick up a girl what are you going to do with her?"

"Walk her to her bus, I guess."

" Yes," Chas went on, more slowly now. "But if you had a car you wouldn't have to go home would you?" He laughed, and immediately I could see endless interesting possibilities

I thought for a moment and asked the question which changed the trajectory of my young life. "What qualifications do you need to be a computer programmer?"

" Two O levels, Maths and English."

Next term at school, my grades started to improve. Slowly at first, and then spectacularly. I guess this was another departure from childhood. I had moved from the realm of not giving a toss and living each day as it came to thinking ahead and trying to do the best I could.

In a short space of time I was promoted to the top class and was soon ahead of most people in that group as well.

Time rolled on, and 1966 was to provide other landmarks. It was the year I was scheduled to take my O levels, and, unknown to my mates, I was working hard. I hadn't forgotten about the computer programmer job, but by now I wanted success for its own sake.

The week before the exams were due to start was half term – Spring Bank Holiday. One night, my brother Nick interrupted my revision at about 6 O'clock on a warm, sunlit evening. My grandad's land had been compulsorily purchased by the council, and Nick and a few of his friends were going to camp out there for the night to say goodbye to it. They were taking some potatoes for roasting.

"It'll be fun, why don't you come?"
I was torn. I had a lot to do but I really wanted to see the old place before it was concreted over.

I was glad that I went because the council had already made a start on clearing the land for building. The orchards and the chicken runs that were our haven of delight when we were younger were already being encroached upon. The fowl sheds had been knocked down and rubble lay around in piles.

When I arrived, Nick was already there with a couple of friends, a guy called Dave and his girlfriend, Iris. Apparently, she was 19, but didn't look it. She was small, with blonde hair, cornflower-blue eyes and a mouth full of gum.

I remember we were lying by the fire and Dave and Nick got

up to go to the local shop to buy some cigarettes or something. After a short while Iris moved close to me.

She blew a bubble with her gum and said, "Would you like to kiss me?"

I remember kissing with our mouths wide open. This was something quite unplanned. Our teeth clashed and then the bubble gum was in my mouth. As I held her I could feel her heart beating like an electric sewing machine motor. Something inside me soared while above us sparks from the fire rose into the sky.

When Nick and Dave came back something had changed, and the world seemed more exciting than ever before.

Chapter 13: Rawlplugs

Somehow I managed to complete my A levels and, after school was over, I applied for a few jobs, but with little enthusiasm or success. I even got turned down by Rexco, apparently work shovelling coke was much sought after. I wasn't too upset.

I applied for a sales rep job selling rawlplugs. I'd never heard of rawlplugs, but the pay seemed to be quite good, and it came with a company car. My brother Richard gave me a lift all the way up to the Queen's Hotel in Leeds where the interview was to take place. All the way there Richard was trying to turn me off the idea, but I was gung-ho for it and was confident that I'd get it.

I was interviewed by a middle-aged man wearing thick black glasses and a very unfashionable tweed jacket. His name was Mr Hunter and he proudly told me that he was something called an Area Sales Manager.

He waited for a response.
I was unnerved. I didn't quite know how to respond, so I just smiled and replied, "Pleased to meet you," and hoped that would do.
I was, however, taken by surprise at his first question
"Tell me, Jonathan, why do you want this position?"

Now, if I had been looking for work down the local pit, I could have anticipated this, but in terms of this job I immediately thought I must be dealing with a moron. Wasn't it obvious?

Well, apparently not. So, I spelt it out, carefully, "Well, two things really, the company car and the money." Mr Hunter looked at me, I could tell he wanted me to elaborate, so I added, "Oh, and a third thing, I really like the idea of being able to go out drinking and being able to drive home."

Mr Hunter looked at me in a way that told me that my answer had impressed him. I figured that he was expecting me to be a little less focussed in my responses and had clearly been used to folks waffling on at length about trivia.

He moved on to the next point. "Well then, can you tell me what you know about rawlplugs."

Jeez, this guy really was an idiot. Why was he asking me about rawlplugs? After all his firm was selling the bloody things. Surely, he should know everything there was to know?

To be honest, if I had had a postage stamp I could have written all I knew, or wanted to know about rawlplugs on the back and still left plenty of room for Mr Hunter to add his six-penn'orth.

I decided to hide my contempt beneath a veil of civility. "I was hoping you'd be able to explain what they are."

Mr Hunter then went on at some length, rather too much length in fact, about rawlplugs, their different sizes, shapes and uses. It gradually dawned on me that basically they were used to help folks put up shelves.

I was beginning to realise that this wasn't the glamour job I was hoping for, and was itching to move on to important things like what sort of car I'd be given and when I'd receive my first pay cheque, but Mr Hunter went on and on, for so long that I began to wonder if he actually inhabited the same universe as me.

According to him, the world as we know would probably cease to exist if it were not for rawlplugs. When our conversation turned to my knowledge of hardware stores I began to drift into a daydream and was toying with my latest favourite word of the week, 'euphemism', when I just caught the words 'Do it Yourself'.

I burst out laughing, I thought Mr Hunter had cracked a joke. "Doesn't it make you go blind?" I asked.

Mr Hunter smiled and drew the interview to a close. I'd obviously done well, after all, I'd answered everything in about half the allocated time. I was, however, doubting whether being Mr Hunter's protégé was really for me, and it was with some relief that a few days later I received a letter regretfully informing me that I was, quote, 'overqualified' for the post.

As a matter of fact, this news came as a relief. I had settled back into sprawling on the settee all day reading pulp WW2 novels while Richard was planning the trip of a lifetime for us, hitchhiking around Europe.

At the end of August we set off on our journey. We caught a boat across the North Sea from Immingham to Amsterdam. It took me, not only from one country to another, but also to another life.

That late summer I encountered students for the first time. I loved their creativity, humour and zest for life, the ease with which they formed friendships and the passion with which they argued and, by the time I came back home from the halcyon summer of '68, I had it firmly fixed in my mind that, if ever I could be a student, I would be.

Things started to kick into place the morning after I got back from my continental adventures. My mum was in the kitchen making coffee.

"Well, now you're back what are you going to do next?"

I was dreading this conversation. After my interview with the bloke from Rawlplugs, and my adventures in Europe, working for a living no longer seemed to be such an attractive prospect.

mum came straight out with it. She was smart, she had a good inkling of what I might really like to do, but she wasn't going to push me.

She lit a cigarette, took a long drag and asked, "Have you thought about going to university?"

"It's too late for that, I needed to have applied months ago."

My mum, though, had been doing some research. "I've been talking to Dave Dabek's brother, he got into university through something called the clearing house, he reckons it's not too late, why don't you give him a call?"

An hour later I was sitting down with Andrew and he gave me the sort of careers information schools never provide.

"To get in, just write letters to each university that you are interested in, and choose a subject like Botany."

"Why Botany?"

He smiled in a knowing way, "There's always spare places on Botany courses because nobody wants to study it."

"What are you studying?"

"Botany. Anyway, don't worry about that. You've got good A levels, including Biology, so I reckon you'll get an offer."

"But I'm not interested in Botany."

"I've told you already, don't worry about that. Just get a place and, when you get there, after about a week or so, tell them that you are unhappy with the course and that you want to change to something that you are actually keen on. It will be a piece of cake."

I took Andrew at his word, went home and wrote letters to the Universities of Liverpool, Newcastle, Manchester and Sheffield. I chose Liverpool for obvious reasons. It was the home of the Beatles, and my brother had once spent a weekend there and hadn't stopped talking about it since.

The other places I knew nothing about apart from the fact that friends of mine had already got places there. Oh yes, one more thing, they all offered degree programmes in my new favourite subject, Botany.

A couple of days I later I was lying in bed when a reply came.

Richard opened it and yelled to me upstairs "You've got a place at Liverpool University."

I jumped up, rushed downstairs and there it was in black and white.

Although I didn't realise it at the time, my future was set, and I'd never live in Kirkby again.

Acknowledgements

Story telling was a bit of a tradition in my family, and much of this book has been around in my head for almost as long as I can remember. My parents, Madge and Harry, my sister Sue and my brothers Richard, Nick, Simon and Adam were probably the first to hear them, but I don't think that I would have ever written them down if not for my kids, Dan, Jess and Harry, constantly badgering me to do so.

So, a couple of years ago, I took the plunge and put pen to paper and began writing and then performing at story telling events in Bristol including 'Talking Tales' and the fabulous 'Let Me Tell You A Story Jack'.

In 2018 I submitted a short story to the 'BBC Upload' programme and, much to my delight, it was played on The Adam Crowther Show, which in turn led to me linking up with a couple of literary mavericks, the author Mike Manson, and Richard Jones at Tangent Books.

I owe a huge debt of gratitude to all these people and organisations, to the town of Kirby in Ashfield and to all the characters who appear in these stories. Most of all though thanks are due to Angie, my wife who has had to listen to these tales over and over again without complaining (too much).